HENDRIX

AXIS: BOLD AS LOVE

THE COMPLETE, AUTHORITATIVE TRANSCRIPTIONS FOR GUITAR, BASS, AND DRUMS

As performed by The Jimi Hendrix Experience, Jimi Hendrix, Mitch Mitchell, and Noel Redding, on the American release version of the Reprise album, *Axis: Bold As Love.*

GW00683529

Guitar Transcriptions by Andy Alerdort and Joff Jones
Bass Transcriptions by Kenn Chipkin
Drum Transcriptions by Kirby Jacobsen
Transcription Supervision and Performance Notes by Dave Whitehill

Photographs by Ken Regan

Music Editor • John Cerullo
Art Director • John Flannery
Editorial Director • Noë "the G" Goldwasser

Photo Research by Bill Nitopi

Released under the supervision of Alan Douglas for Bella Godiva Music, Inc.

Exclusive distributors for EC and EFTA countries (United Kingdom, Eire, Norway,
Denmark, Sweden, Finland, Belgium, Holland, Luxembourg, France, Germany, Italy,
Spain, Portugal, Greece, Austria and Switzerland) and Australasia:
Music Sales Limited, 8/9 Frith Street, London W1V 5TZ.
Music Sales Pty Limited, 120 Rothschild Avenue, Rosebery, NSW 2018, Australia.

15.95
m

CONTENTS

INTRODUCTION

A VOYAGE TO THE COSMOS

JIMI HENDRIX RECORDED THE THIRTEEN STELLAR TRACKS OF *AXIS: Bold As Love* in 1967, in the wake of his tremendous reception at Monterey and the huge impact that *Are You Experienced?* and the outrageousness of his music had begun to make on the youth of the world. The generation that embraced Jimi was going through its changes, experimenting with new lifestyles and rebellion, and developing its own culture of flamboyant dress and extravagant gesture. They were ready for Jimi, and he was willing to take them out, showing them the brave new worlds that one could see by the light of the stars, if only one would dare to fly.

Jimi's energetic stage manner and much-vaunted pyrotechnics inspired headlines and newspaper copy wherever they went. By the Summer of Love, Jimi, Mitch, and Noel had been touring the States as their music broke on the American airwaves. They played the Fillmore in San Francisco to the tumultuous acclaim of that town's hippies and freaks, and they returned to England in August to put the finishing touches on *Axis* and to gird themselves for the months of heavy touring that would set the stage for its release, which occurred in November, 1967. The band played material from the new album as they toured Europe through the end of that year, and continued their primal assault on America in 1968.

If *Experienced?* can be seen as a thunderbolt that released shock waves through the minds of those in its path, *Axis* is a comet on its way to outer space with Jimi sitting right on top of it, saying, "Hop on board!" The spacey sound of the album, as captured by producer Chas Chandler and the brilliant engineer Eddie Kramer, is deeper, more spiritual, and musically self-indulgent than that of its predecessor. Nowhere is this more evident than on the title track, "Bold As Love" (which ends the album on the American version, but for some inexplicable reason is sandwiched in the middle of side two on the English release. Unlike *Experienced?*, there are no track substitutions, only a slight difference of track order between this and the Brit release.) After Jimi states his ballad theme, accented by droning, bluesy riffs on the middle strings, Mitch's tom-toms lead into a coda of absolutely magnificent, lyrical guitar work that is phased and processed as it flies around the universe. The same kind of processing is carried to the nth degree on the album's opener, "EXP," after the intro rap to the "spaceman" Paul Corusoe.

Hendrix' guitar—and parts of "Paul Revere's Ride," feedback, radio noise, and a mess of other sounds get melanged through Eddie Kramer's audio meat-grinder as they go careening from speaker to speaker and—again—out to outer space.

The mystical nature of the album is heightened by Jimi's intimate vocal textures, the studio mikes catching his philosophical asides and metaphysical ramblings, as on the anthemic "If 6 Was 9," as he muses about the uniqueness of his own iconoclastic lifestyle: "Dig— 'cause I got my own world to live through and I ain't gonna copy you." Then, the inimitable oratorio of ..."white-collared conservative flashin' down the street, pointing their plastic finger at me... I'm gonna wave my freak flag high!...Go on, Mr. Businessman, you can't dress like me....I got my own life to live. I'm the one who's got to die when it's time for me to die. So let me live my life the way I want to." And once that epitome of bohemianism and cosmic far-outness is uttered, Hendrix goes off into the outer limits again with his guitar and his wah-wah pedal and a million other sonic gadgets.

Throughout the album, Hendrix swings on the axis of the universe, feeling his sonic oats and spouting wisdom and beautiful melodies like he was breathing them—which he was. The man had so many musical ideas coursing through him all the time that he couldn't wait to write them down, scribbling on pieces of paper or improvising with his guitar. And so, *Axis: Bold As Love* stands today as a record of that magical obsession, and we who study it here in tranquility may benefit from its bounty. Though much of it has to do with studio trickery and experimentation, all of it is built on the solid musicianship and the artistic vision of the man who invented it, and the deftness of the two frizzy-haired cohorts who drove the engine with bass and drums and rode along with him on those flights of fancy, keeping up with him as only the most intimate of partners could.

We've tried to keep this in mind as we laid out this volume, with its exact and exacting transcriptions of bass, drum, and guitar parts. There is much to be learned by modern musicians from these written-out footprints of posterity. You will notice in studying these charts that the dance was highly choreographed. Not only did these three guys click on a cosmic level, but all their moves depended on precision timing and orchestration—and a profound musical vision.

—Noë "the G" Goldwasser
Founding Editor, *Guitar World*
Series Editor, *The Hendrix Transcriptions*

BEAUTIFUL "NOISE," ELABORATE SOUNDSCAPES, AND UNUSUAL COLORISTIC EFFECTS ON THE GUITAR ARE ALL A PART OF Hendrix' musical legacy, but in some instances they still remain a bit of an enigma, a tough nut to crack for transcribers sifting through the sands of time.

Harmonic and microphonic feedback are the main components of this piece, but only the former could be accurately—albeit subjectively—notated. This type of feedback is directly related to the harmonic overtone series and may be initiated in several ways. One surefire method is to lightly touch a vibrating open string at the proper position or node while in close proximity to the amp. For example, if the fifth string were ringing out an open A and you wanted feedback an octave above that, you'd just make brief contact with the string directly over the twelfth fret. If done at the seventh fret instead, the result will be E, an octave and a fifth above open A; at the fifth, an even higher A; at the fourth, C#, and so on.

Fundamental tone (same as the actual pitch) feedback is readily achieved by placing the headstock of your guitar against the speaker cabinet. Experiment with the vibrato bar, combine the two aforementioned techniques, and make some of your own close encounters of the "Third Stone" kind.

EXP

Words and Music by JIMI HENDRIX

Announcer: *Good evening ladies and gentlemen.*
Welcome to radio station EXP.
Tonight we are featuring an interview with a very peculiar looking gentleman,
who goes by the name of Mr. Paul Corusoe on the dodgy subject of: are there
or are there not flying saucers or...ahem, UFO's?

Um...Please, Mr. Corusoe, could you give us your regarded opinion on this
nonsense about spaceships, and even space people?

Mr. Corusoe: *Thank you.*
As you all know, you just can't believe everything you see and hear. Can you?
Now, if you'll excuse me, I must be on my way.

Announcer: *Bu...but, but...glub.....I, I don't believe it.*

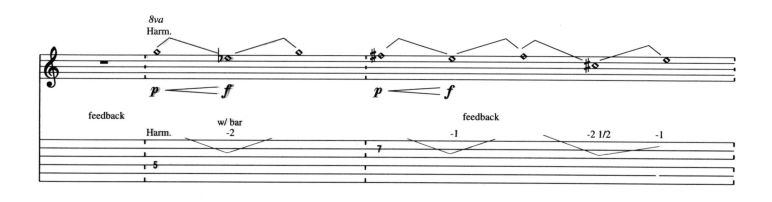

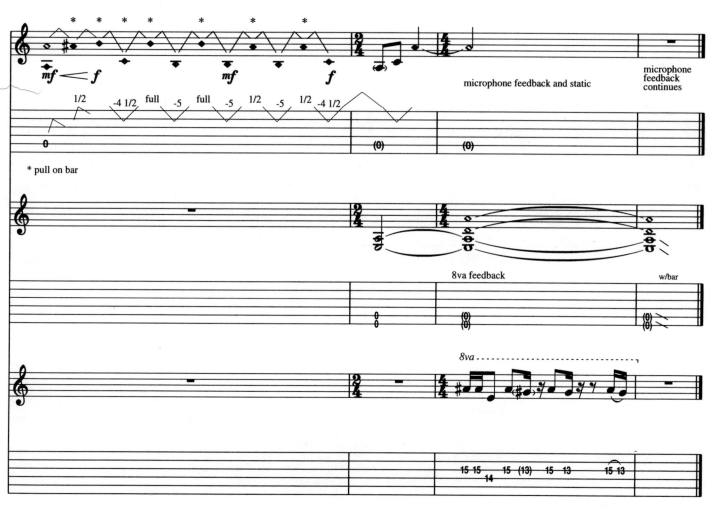

UP FROM THE SKIES

"EXP" SEGUÉS INTO THIS SONG CONCERNING A VISITING EXTRA-TERRESTRIAL AND ITS QUERIES REGARDING LIFE ON THIS PLANET, PROVIDing some subtle tongue-in-cheek social commentary in the process. Meanwhile, a "jazzy" groove is laid down by a trio of Earth denizens: Mitch (with brushes in hand), Jimi (with wah-wah pedal at foot), and Noel.

Note that the guitar accompaniment throughout the verses has been reduced to a chord-chart type of format. For greater ease of reading, you'll need to refer to the chord diagrams in order to achieve the correct voicings. Incidentally, if these forms, with their numerical designations, are "alien" to you and you're curious as to their origin, then check out your library for textbooks dealing with basic harmony. Some additional information may also be found in the player's notes for "If 6 was 9."

UP FROM THE SKIES

Words and Music by JIMI HENDRIX

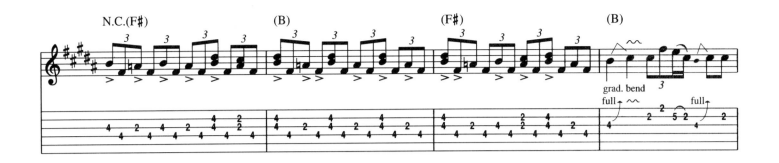

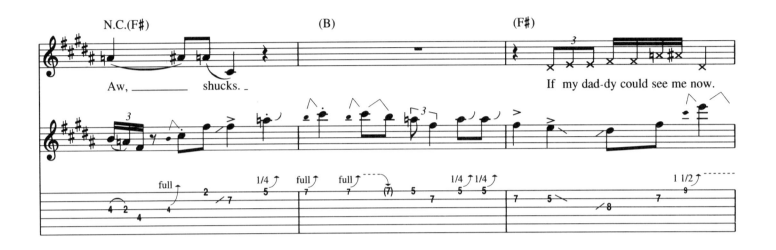

Aw, _____ shucks. _

If my dad-dy could see me now.

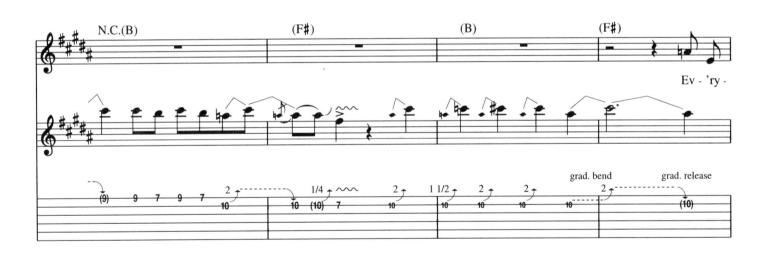

Ev - 'ry -

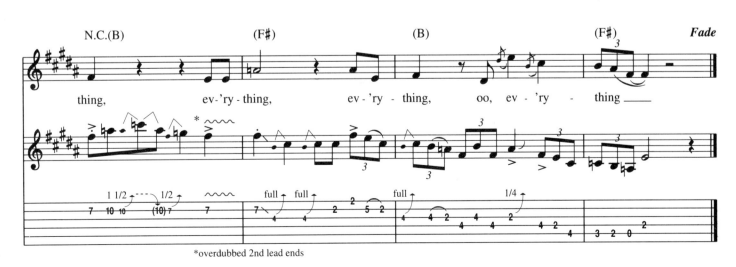

thing,   ev - 'ry - thing,   ev - 'ry - thing,   oo, ev - 'ry - thing ____

*overdubbed 2nd lead ends

SPANISH CASTLE MAGIC

MANY OF JIMI'S COMPOSITIONS WERE WRITTEN IN KEY SIGNATURES NOT NORMALLY ASSOCIATED WITH ROCK MUSIC. THIS ONE, FOR instance, is in C#, an apt choice, since it allows the main riff's lowest note, the flatted third, to be played on the open sixth and the open first and second strings to be used in conjunction with the C#7 #9.

The chromatic progression is also fairly avant-garde for the rock idiom, but Hendrix always had a penchant for the unusual and strived to avoid blatant musical clichés. Examine any of his solos and you'll find at least one little twist or a variation on a familiar theme. Note that in "Spanish Castle Magic"'s bridge solo there is an abundance of uncommonly bent notes, starting with a minor third bend from C# to E in the first measure at beat 4. Jimi then bends up to the major sixth in the next measure and later does some novel double-stop bends, especially the last one. There's simply a wealth of ideas to glean from this solo, so learn it verbatim and then incorporate these "gems" into your lead breaks.

SPANISH CASTLE MAGIC

Words and Music by JIMI HENDRIX

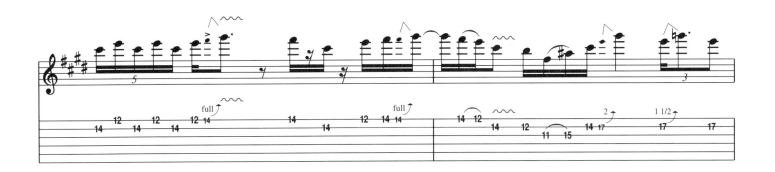

Ah!

Chorus

A

N.C.(F#m7)

Hang ___ on, ____ my dar - ling. ___ Hey!

WAIT UNTIL TOMORROW

ON THE BASIS OF HIS SINGULAR STYLE OF STORYTELLING, BOTH IN LYRIC CONTENT AND ACCOMPANYING GUITAR PARTS, HENDRIX COULD have been the Mark Twain of rock. For instance, note in measure 3 of the third verse that as he queries, "Do I see a silhouette..." the guitar seemingly says, "Uh-oh" on beat 3 with the introduction of a G major chord against A in the bass.

The use of pedal point is constant throughout the choruses. While Jimi plays figures based on the progression: I - bIII - IV (E, G and A major), Noel's part is centered around the tonic. During the first half of this chord cycle he repeatedly plays "sliding sixths," a fave of Steve Cropper's. This intervallic structure requires the second string to be muffled by the middle finger while it is simultaneously fretting the third string. The same technique is applicable to the playing of octaves, as in"Third Stone From The Sun" off of "Are You Experienced?" and other wide intervals.

Throughout the verses Jimi uses a rather sophisticated concept involving harmonic extensions of the dominant chord built on the fifth degree of a scale, in this case, the major scale. Since the verse modulates to A major, the root of the dominant is an E major triad (E G# B), and by placing a series of thirds above it results in a thirteenth chord. Noting that other triads other than E major are within its superstructure of E G# B D F# A C#, it's possible to take them out of context as Hendrix does commencing with measure 2 of each verse.

WAIT UNTIL TOMORROW

Words and Music by JIMI HENDRIX

* Only basic tonality represented by chord names due to degree of chordal ornamentations

AIN'T NO TELLING

BEGINNING WITH THE "CALL AND RESPONSE" OPENING, YOU'LL NOTE THERE IS SOME MARVELOUS INTERPLAY between the guitars in this song, especially during the bridge and the instrumental interlude that follows. Throughout the bridge, guitar 1 repeats an ostinato pattern consisting of the tonic and supertonic, C# and D#, while guitar 2 "walks" with the bass. This is followed by a brief modulation to the distant key of A major for the duration of a four measure contrapuntal instrumental interlude reminiscent of the bridge solo for "The Wind Cries Mary."

As in "Spanish Castle Magic" (which was also in C# major) the use of the dominant seventh with the augmented ninth, Jimi's favorite altered chord, gives this song a major/minor ambiguity since the raised ninth is enharmonic to the minor third.

AIN'T NO TELLING

Words and Music by JIMI HENDRIX

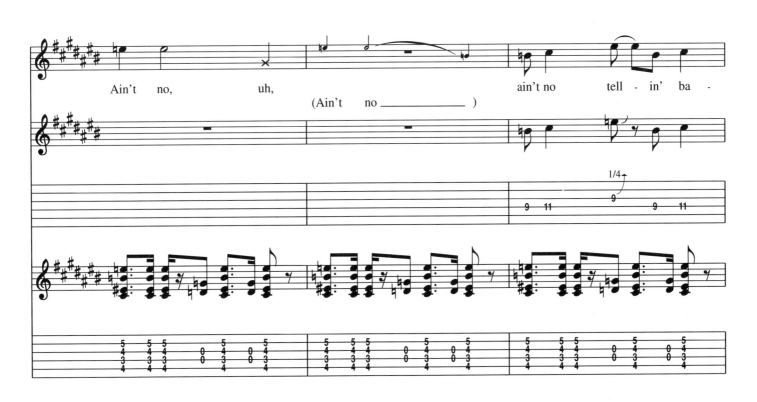

Oh, Cle - o - pa - tra, she's driv-in' me in-sane, she's try-in' to put my bod-y

in her brain. So, uh, just uh,

kiss me good bye, just to ease the pain.

must leave now.

unison bends _ _ _ _ _ _ _

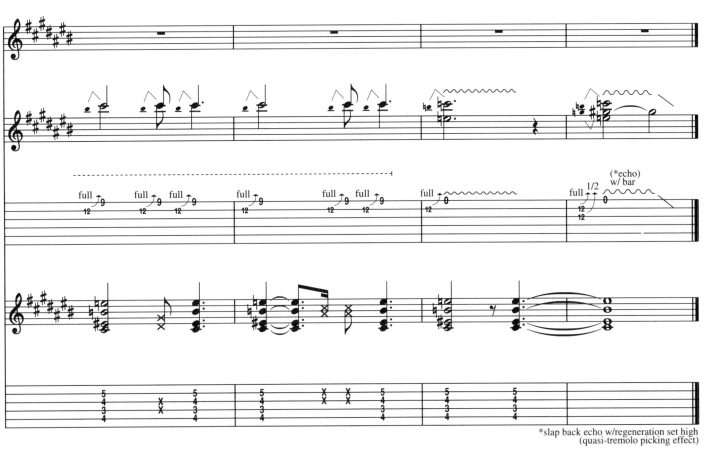

*slap back echo w/regeneration set high
(quasi-tremolo picking effect)

LITTLE WING

JIMI'S PROTEAN IMAGINATION IS EVIDENT IN HIS UNIQUE CHORDAL STYLE, PARTICULARLY IN A BALLAD LIKE "LITTLE WING." IN THIS CONtext, his approach to the guitar is more like that of a pianist: Jimi breaks away from the confines of the dogmatic "rhythm or lead" method. His thumb frets the bass notes, functioning in almost the same manner as a keyboardist's left hand, and the fingers of his fretting hand can be likened to a pianist's right hand. Let's examine a few excerpts that demonstrate this piano style format and rediscover what Adrian Belew has called a "lost art."

On the first beat of measure 2 Jimi frets the root of the G major chord with his thumb, allowing it to be sustained as he follows up with the chord melody. Although the melody is within the third position form of G major, the complete chord is not fingered at any one time. Jimi usually plays diads (double stops) and movement within these partial chords is oblique; that is, one pitch is stationary. If you examine measure 6 you'll find extensive use of oblique motion.

Going to the second verse, an example of parallel motion can be found in measure 2, as the interval of a fourth is slid back and forth over a distance of a whole tone. This idea based on the major pentatonic scale also appears in the coda to "The Wind Cries Mary."

The unusual tonal quality of Jimi's guitar is characteristic of the pickup combination known as the "out-of-phase" mode (see text for "One Rainy Wish"). The ethereal effect beginning with measure 6 is the result of playing through a unit associated with organists, the rotating speaker cabinet or "Leslie." Actually, it's the speaker baffle that moves, creating slow or fast vibration on the principle of the Doppler effect.

LITTLE WING

Words and Music by JIMI HENDRIX

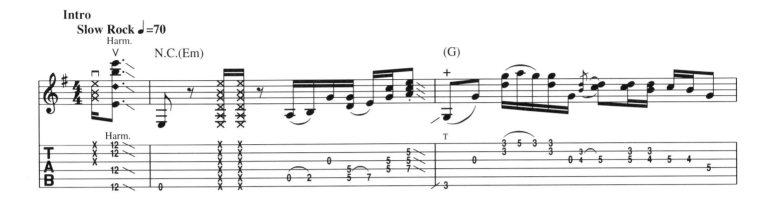

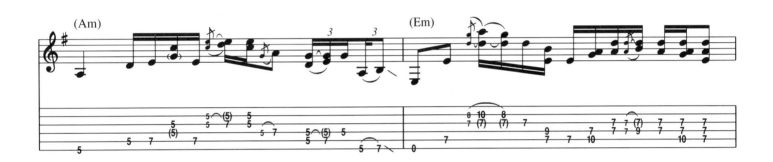

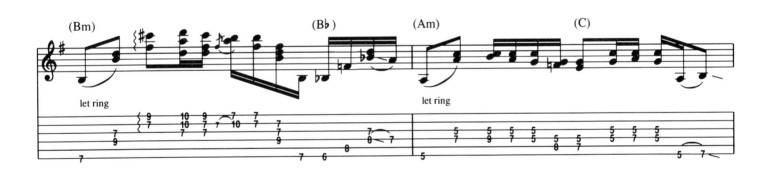

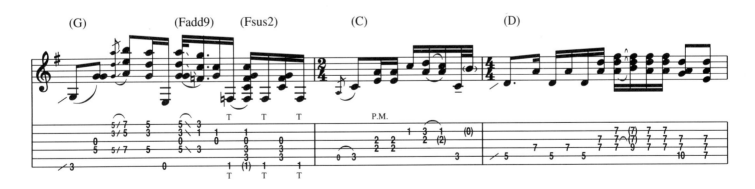

with a thou - sand smiles _ she gives to me _ free. _

It's al - right, she _ says _ it's al - right, _ take an - y - thing _ you want _

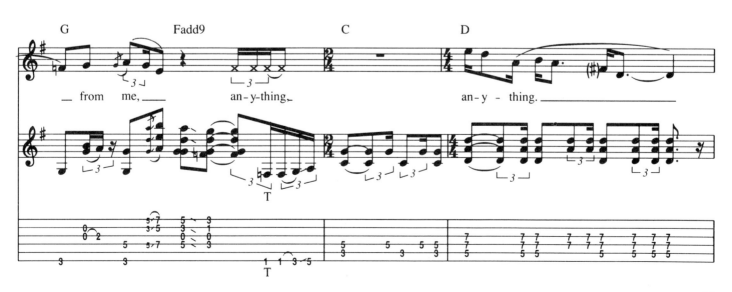

_ from me, _ an - y - thing _ an - y - thing. _

IF 6 WAS 9

ONE OUTSTANDING FEATURE OF THIS SONG IS THAT DURING THE VERSES JIMI DOUBLES HIS VOCAL LINE WITH THE GUITAR. THIS DEVICE WAS first used, but to a much lesser extent, in the guitar solo to "Manic Depression" from *Are You Experienced?* There, it was done in unison instead of an octave below his voice, as found here.

Moving along to the conclusion of the verse, the format switches to chordal accompaniment and the song's momentum builds. Jimi's penchant for lush, complex voicings is evident as he opts for the dominant seventh chord with a suspension of a second (7 sus2) for the first three chords in this descending progression. From a theoretical standpoint, this form naturally occurs when harmonizing on the dominant or fifth degree of a major scale. For example, if we took the D major scale (D E F# G A B C#) and began constructing a chord on A, the fifth degree, by superimposing intervals of a third (tertian harmony) our first true chord would be a major triad consisting of A, C#, and E. Continuing in the same manner will result in various harmonic extensions (7, 9,11, and 13), but for our purposes we'll just require the seventh, G, and then replace the third, C#, with the second, B, for the required suspension.

IF 6 WAS 9

Words and Music by JIMI HENDRIX

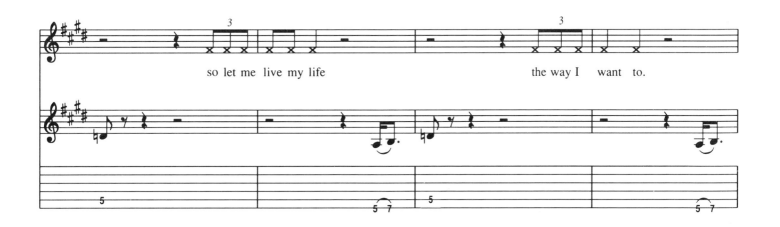

so let me live my life   the way I want to.

There,____   sing on broth- er,

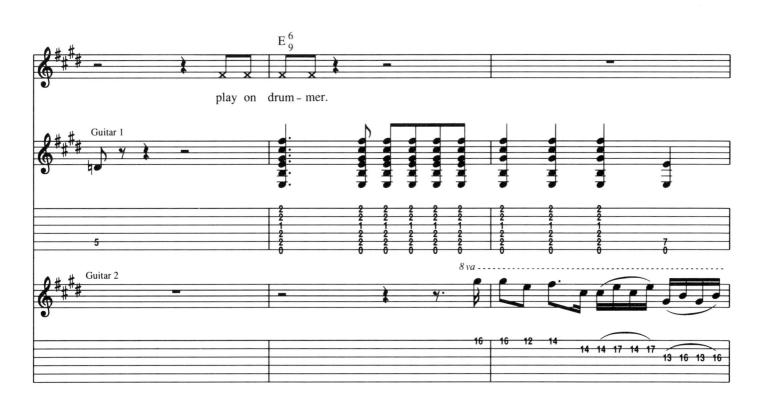

play on drum - mer.

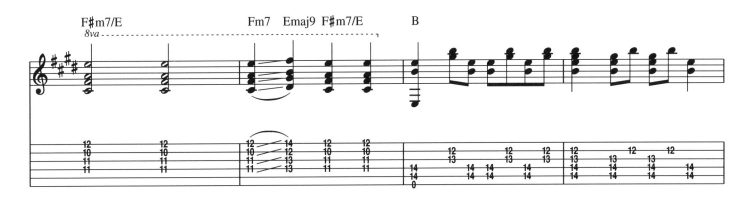

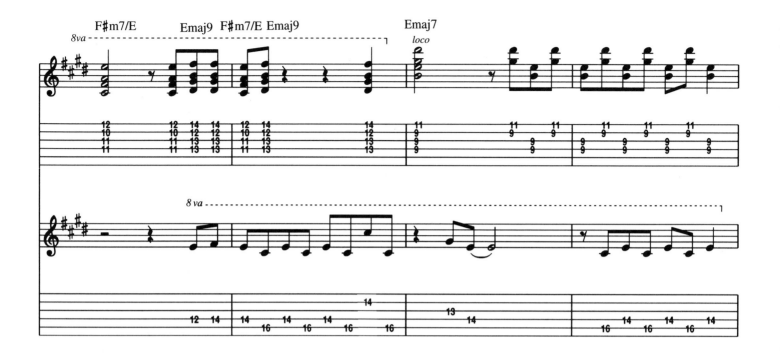

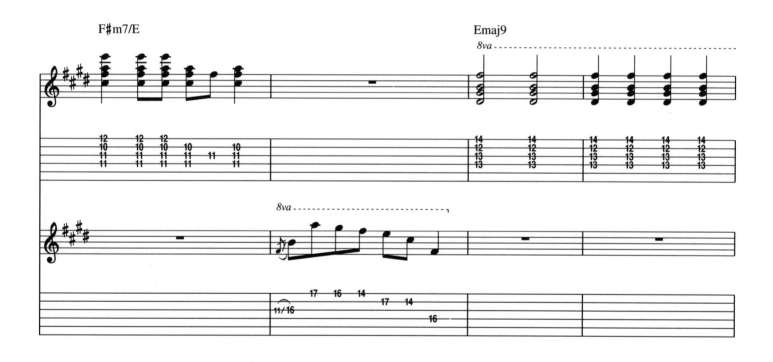

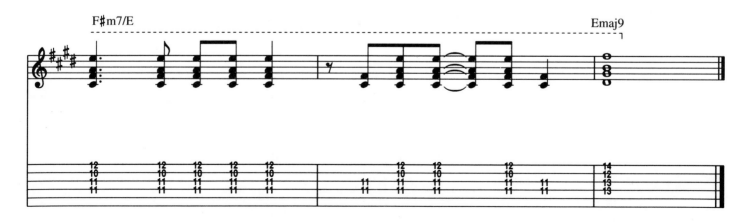

YOU GOT ME FLOATIN'

THE OPENING GUITAR FIGURE IS IN "REVERSE" THROUGH MANIPULATION OF THE TAPE AS ON "ARE YOU Experienced?" from the first lp. Check out the accompanying notes to that song for a detailed account of this recording technique and optional methods of replicating the "backwards" effect.

Jimi then shifts into "drive" with the funky main riff, resplendent with sharply attacked partial chords and muted strings. Note that all muting is done by the fretting hand versus the traditional palm mute.

The most notable feature of this cut has to do with its novel instrumentation. An eight-string bass is used in this piece and is prominent in the bridge solo as it is played in counterpoint to the guitar. For those of you unfamiliar to this type of bass, it is similar to the four-string variety except for adjunct strings an octave higher to give the effect of a guitar doubling the bass part.

YOU GOT ME FLOATIN'

Words and Music by JIMI HENDRIX

got   me float – in',   float __ to please.   Got __ me float – in'.
                    float – in'

Ooh.

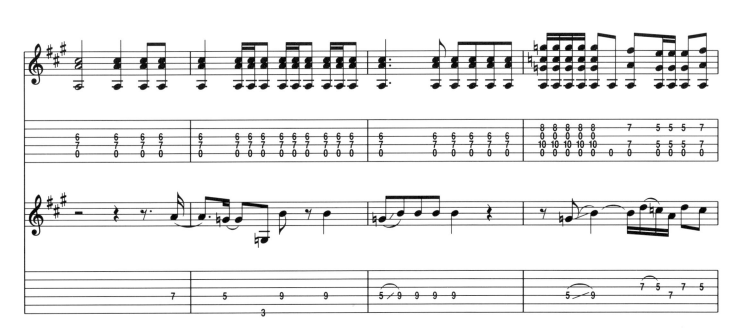

Background: Got me float - in' round _____ and round. You

Lead: Yeah! _____ Gim-me one more time, broth-er, say it.

Got me float - in', nev - er down. _____ You

Got me float - in', yeah. _____

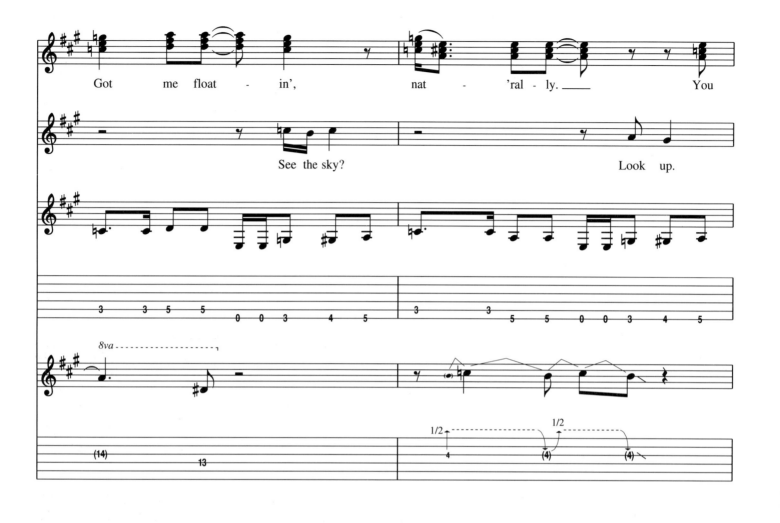

Dad-dy's cool and your mom-ma's no fool. ___ They both know ___ I'm head o-ver

heels ___ for you. And when the day melts down in - to a sleep-y, red glow, ___ that's

when my de - sires ___ start to show.

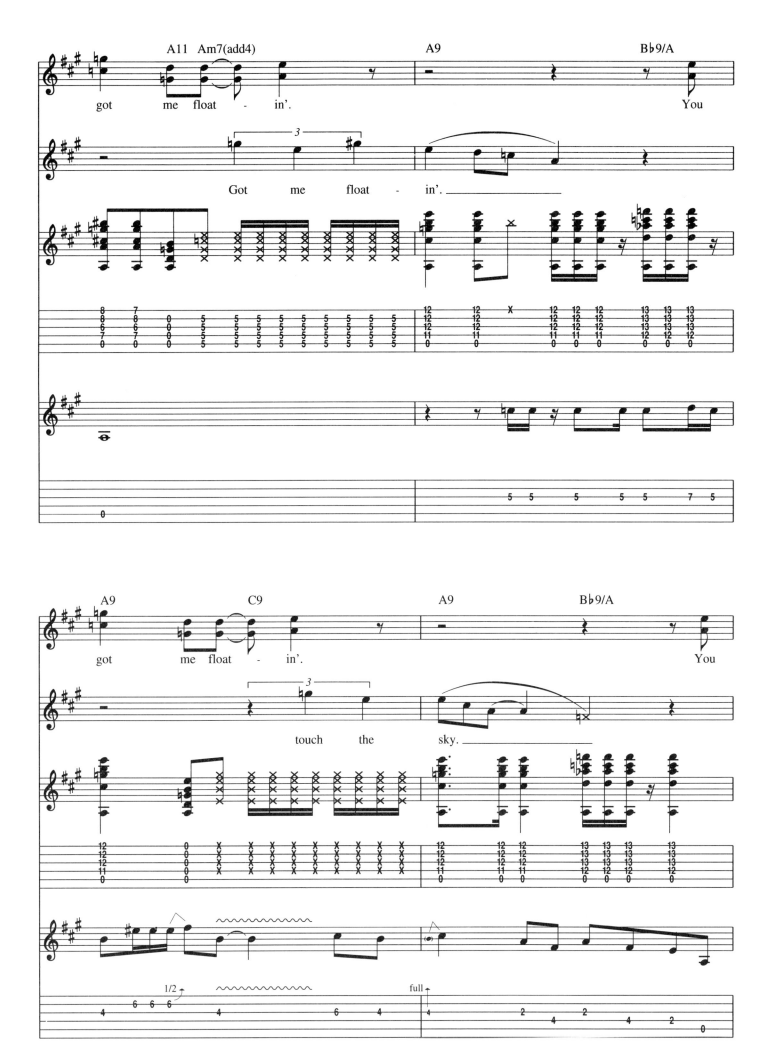

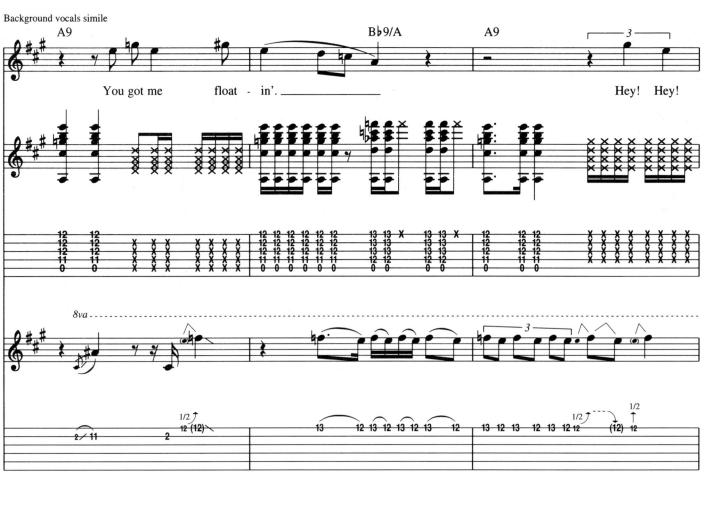

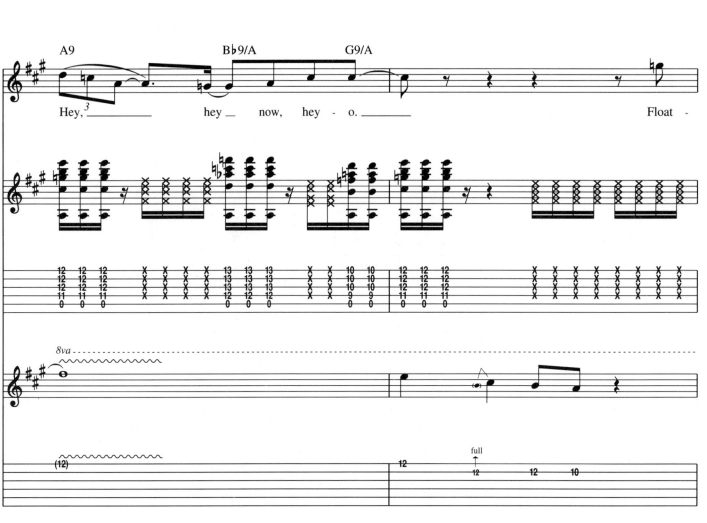

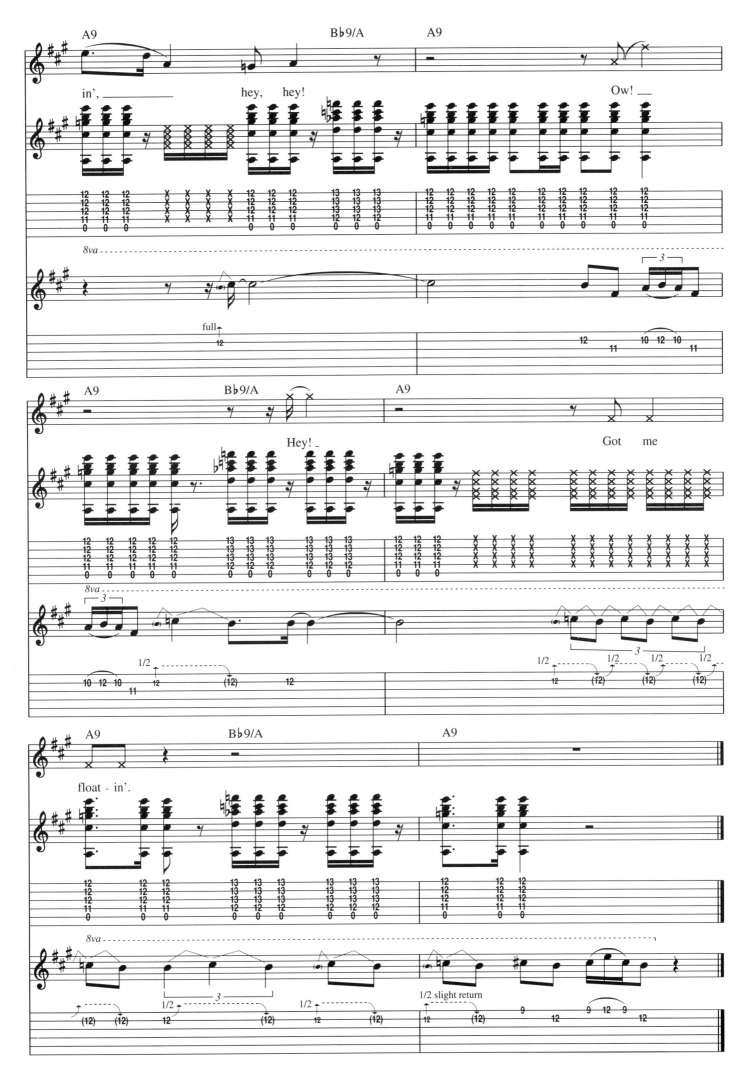

CASTLES MADE OF SAND

WHEREAS JIMI'S ANTHEM TO NONCONFORMITY, "IF 6 WAS 9," WAS VEHEMENTLY SUBJECTIVE IN ITS DECLARATIONS, HERE HE IS more or less a detached observer of life's ironies. There's even a certain pathos to the music itself which can be attributed to the fact that there are brief departures from the major mode to minor.

The first voicing, G5 add 9 (also called G sus2) has a rather bittersweet quality to it, being neither "fish nor fowl" (i.e. major nor minor), and then Bb, the minor third, is introduced by virtue of the parallel movement of the opening chordal figure and its recapitulation at the song's conclusion. Note also that the minor mode is inferred by the entrance of a Bb major chord in the last measures of the introduction.

As in "You Got Me Floating," there's that ubiquitous "backwards" guitar in the background, and this time it is also the solo instrument.

Memorization of this song is a must for any guitar-slinging Hendrix devotee. Just ask Frank Marino of Mahogany Rush fame, an "honor student" of the Jimi Hendrix school of guitar.

CASTLES MADE OF SAND

Words and Music by JIMI HENDRIX

* all phrases fade in due to nature of effect
(i.e. "backwards" guitar)

Verse 1 Fsus2

Down the street you can hear her scream, "You're a dis-grace," as she

N.C. Am   Em7

slams the door   in his drunk-en face, _   and now he stands _ out - side _ and all the

F   C   G

neigh - bors start to gos - sip and   drool. _____   He _

Verse 2

* vibrato G intermittently "bumping into" C note, 3rd string, 5th fret

in the sea, ____ e - ven - tu - al - ly.

A lit - tle In - di - an brave_ who, be - fore he was ten, __ played

war games in the woods_ with his In - di - an friends,_ and he built a dream that when he grew up he would

There _

Verse 3

was a young girl_ whose heart was a frown_ 'cause she was crip-pled for life _ and she could-n't speak a sound, _ and she

wished and prayed _ she could stop liv-in', so she de - cid-ed to die.

Gsus2 F#5 Fsus2

She drew her wheel-chair to the edge ___ of the shore, and to _

A5 Em7

_ her legs she smiled,_"You won't hurt me no more."___ But then a sight she'd nev-er seen _ made her jump and say

F6 C5 G

"Look, a gold-en winged ship is pass-ing my way." (spoken): And it real-ly did-n't

Guitar 1

let ring

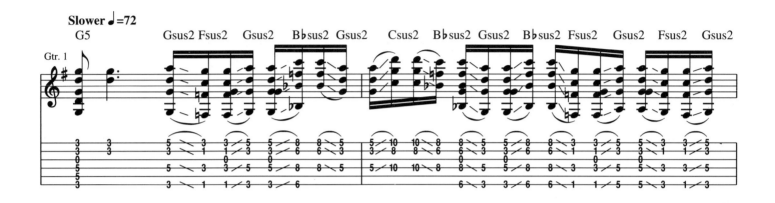

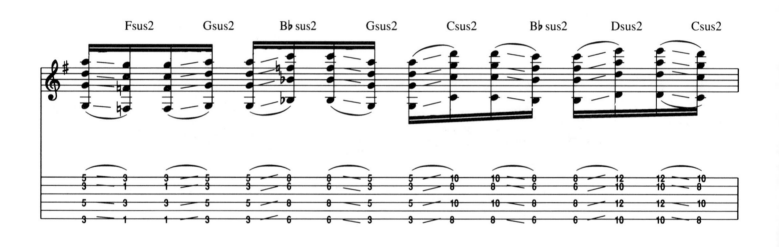

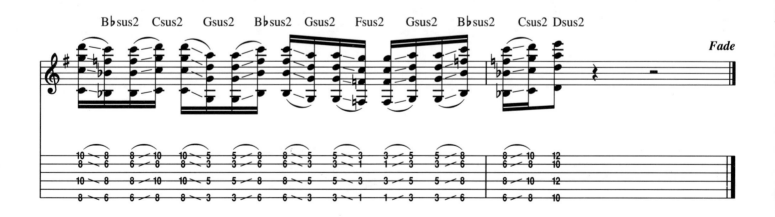

SHE'S SO FINE

NOEL REDDING MADE HIS SONGWRITING AND LEAD VOCAL DEBUT ON *AXIS: BOLD AS LOVE* WITH THIS COMPOSI-
tion. Decidedly in a psychedelic pop vein, this song is based primarily on the A mixolydian mode (A B
C# D E F# G), which differs from the major scale or ionian mode in that the seventh degree is lowered.
One exception is in the verses when D is the temporary tonal center, as in measures 13-16; at this point
in the progression the D mixolydian (D E F# G A B C) replaces the A.

Throughout the verses Jimi's fills are either derived from the A major pentatonic scale (A B C# E F#)
or the aforementioned mixolydian modes. The bridge solo is in G and the lead lines the G major pentatonic scale with the addition of the fourth (G A B C D E).

As far as technique goes, the only sections you may experience a bit of difficulty with are where two
adjacent strings are bent in parallel fashion, as in, for example, measures 19-20. This bend will require
particular attention to intonation as well as some strong fingers.

SHE'S SO FINE

Words and Music by NOEL REDDING

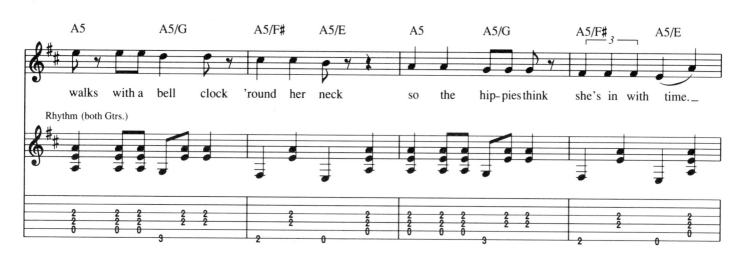

walks with a bell clock 'round her neck so the hip-pies think she's in with time.

la la la la la la la la.

*bend on only ③ ; hold previous bend on ②.

*bend continues on only ③ (third string).

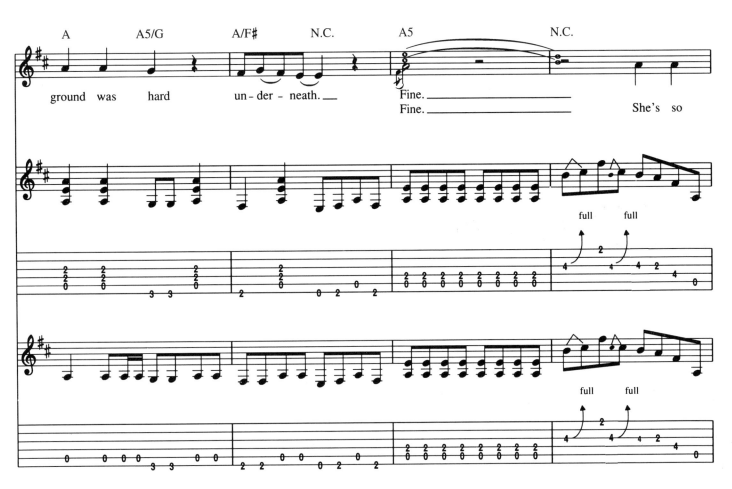

ONE RAINY WISH

ANOTHER OF JIMI'S "HONOR STUDENTS," ERIC JOHNSON, CITES THIS ODE TO A DREAM AS ONE OF HIS PERSONAL FAVORITES. IT'S ALSO near the top of my list, primarily for its aesthetic appeal, but it has a sufficient amount of radical Hendrixian harmonic and rhythmic concepts to warrant some lenghty academically-minded musings.

To my knowledge, this was the first rock song to have the verse and chorus in different time signatures. Up 'til the last measure of the first verse it is in triple meter, 3/4 time, which is then replaced by the double meter, 4/4 time, of the chorus.

The harmonies contain numerous Jimi signatures, most notably by guitar 2 starting with the opening E major add sixth chord and harmonization of the E major pentatonic scale (E F# G# B C#) in fourths, commencing with measure 5 to the exquisite A major add 9 voicing in the second measure of the verse. The guitar also has a decidedly "nasal" quality to it, due to the fact that the bridge and middle pickups were engaged simultaneously. This was before the advent of five-way pickup selectors on Stratocasters and Jimi attained this setting—erroneously dubbed by most as the "out-of-phase" mode—by first removing the spring from its precursor, the three-way switch. This setting is also employed in "Castles Made Of Sand," "Wait Until Tomorrow," and "Ain't No Telling."

ONE RAINY WISH

Words and Music by JIMI HENDRIX

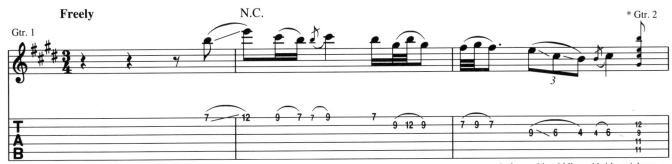

* clean with middle and bridge pickups on

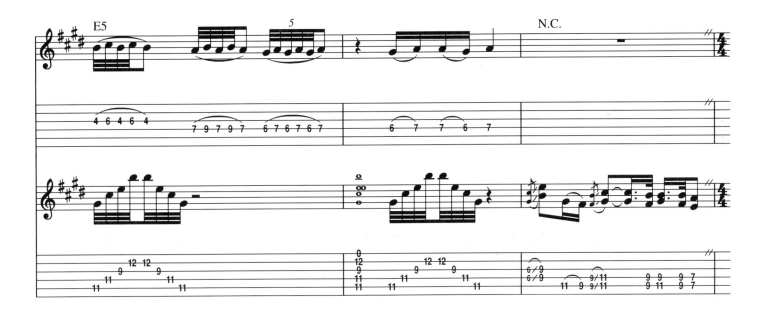

Gold and _ rose the col-or of the dream I had, not too long_____ a -

played ___ a-cross the rain - bows.   a- bove   me and you.

8va

C#m

Gold   and ___ rose   the col-or of the vel-vet walls   (that) sur-round   us.

8va

8va

LITTLE MISS LOVER

MITCH MITCHELL'S INTRO FIGURE TO "LITTLE MISS LOVER" EXEMPLIFIES HIS UNCANNY KNACK for creating drum parts on Hendrix' riffs. Other examples can be found in the introductions to "I Don't Live Today" and "Voodoo Child (Slight Return)".

Throughout the verses Jimi's guitar assumes the character of a percussion instrument, the result of using a wah-wah pedal in conjunction with muted strings. Going into the lead break he switches on his Octavia, playing a solo that practically covers the gamut of bends idiomatic to the rock and blues genre. Just in case you're a novice to string-bending, take heed and be sure to place all available digits behind the finger executing the bend for additional leverage and support. Most bends are done with the ring finger of the fretting hand, so your index and middle fingers will be the ones assisting in pushing a string up to the required pitch.

LITTLE MISS LOVER

Words and Music by JIMI HENDRIX

oh __ look at me with soul   here   so __ good. _____   Lit - tle Miss Lov-er.

Hey,   ba-by   oh!

She makes ev-'ry-thing good,   lit-tle Miss Lov - er.

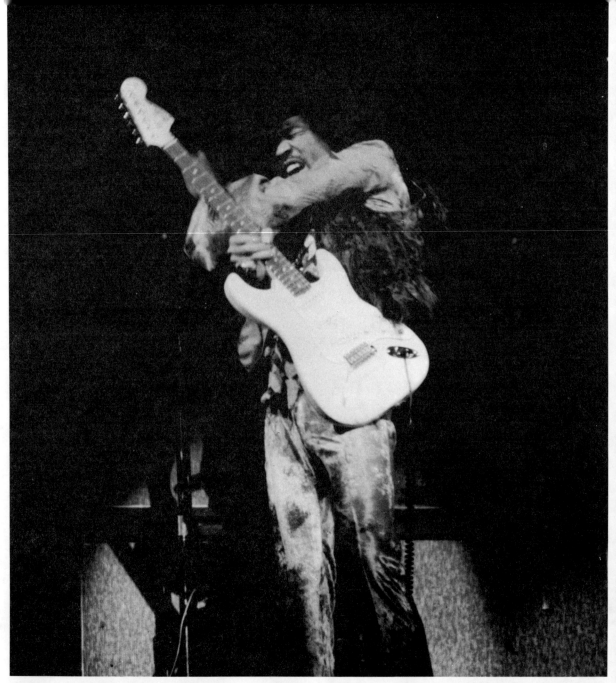

BOLD AS LOVE

THE FLOWER OF JIMI'S LYRICAL GENIUS IS IN FULL BLOOM THROUGHOUT *AXIS: BOLD AS LOVE*, ESPECIALLY THE TITLE CUT, WITH ITS imagery and personification of the colors. "Lyrical" is also an apt adjective for his guitar playing, whether it be the chordal counterpoint within the verses or the lead lines during the majestic coda.

Examining the bridge solo from a theoretical standpoint will reveal why it works in relationship to the chord progression and should help you in developing your own melodies. Harmonic and nonharmonic tones are the "yin and yang" of melody, a dichotomy in which each note is either part of or foreign to the accompanying chord. For example, the solo commences on the root of the A major chord in the form of a unison bend, then it moves along to roots of the next two chords in the progression, E major and F# minor. In the third and fifth measures he bends to C#, which is the third of the A major triad(A C# E), then releases it back to B, the fifth of the E major triad (E G# B).

Following this section, Mitch plays a brief solo interlude wherein his drums are colored by ace engineer Eddie Kramer with a bit of studio magic known as flanging. Current state-of-the-art technology makes this effect available electronically, but when *Axis: Bold As Love* was produced it was done mechanically. This required manipulating the reel flange (projecting rim) to one of two tape decks, running simultaneously, with the thumb and mixing the resulting signal.

The music of the majestic grand finale seems to take flight and "kiss the sky" on its new course of C# major. Note that beginning with measure 11 Jimi uses arpeggios, a trademark of his disciple Yngwie Malmsteen, based on the C# - G# - A#m - B progression and fades out with tremolo picked partial chords.

BOLD AS LOVE

Words and Music by JIMI HENDRIX

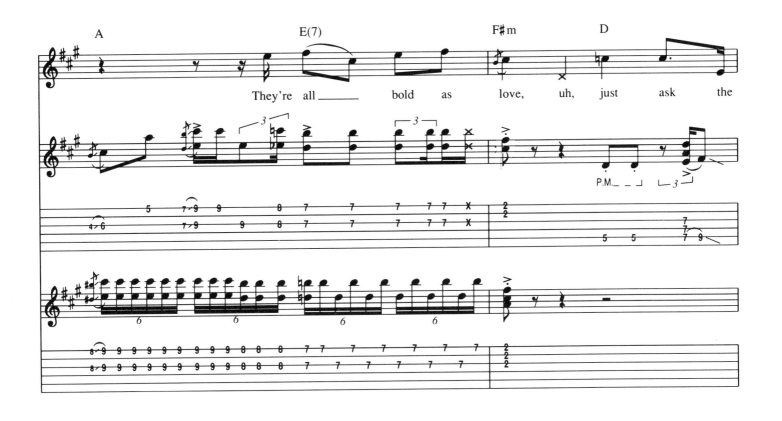

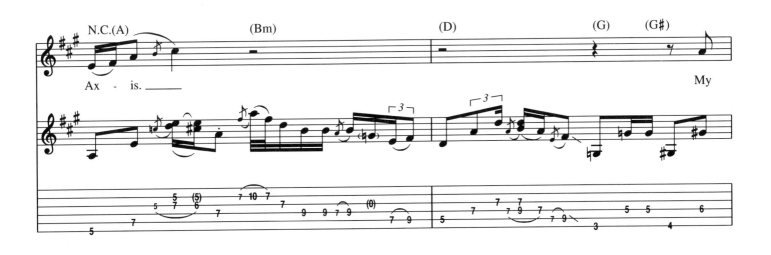

Chorus

giv - ing my life to a rain - bow like you, but I'm, uh,

Yeah, I'm bold __ as love, __ yeah, yeah. __

Well, I'm __ bold, __ bold __ as love, __ hear me talk- in', girl.

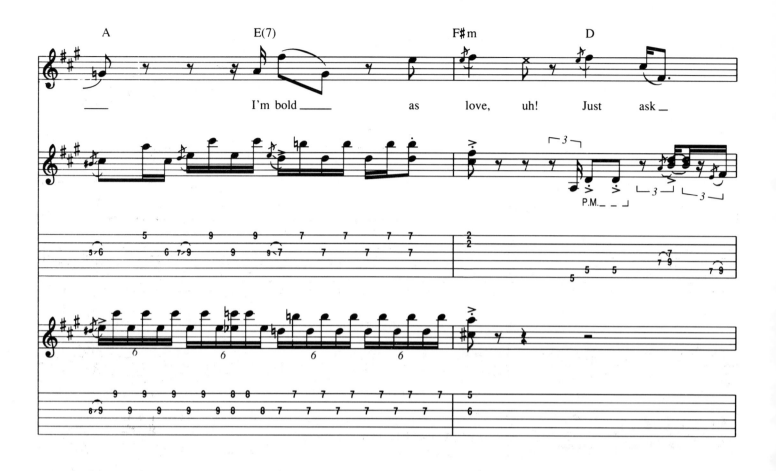

I'm bold _____ as love, uh! Just ask _____

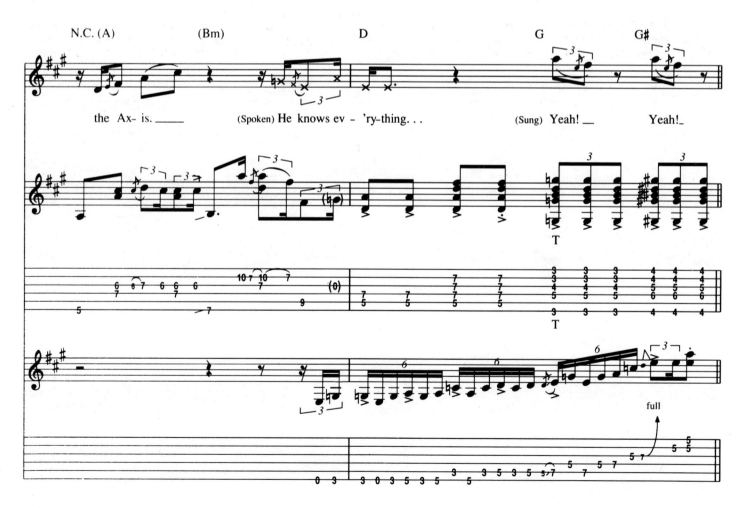

the Ax- is. _____ (Spoken) He knows ev - 'ry-thing... (Sung) Yeah! _____ Yeah!_

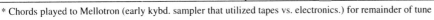

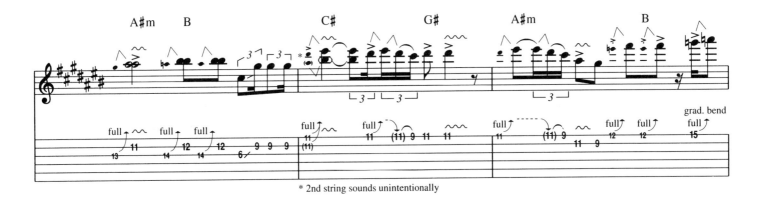

* Chords played to Mellotron (early kybd. sampler that utilized tapes vs. electronics.) for remainder of tune

* 2nd string sounds unintentionally

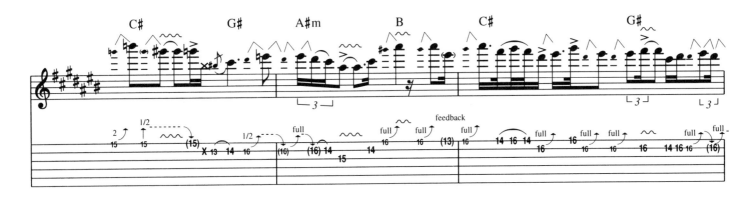

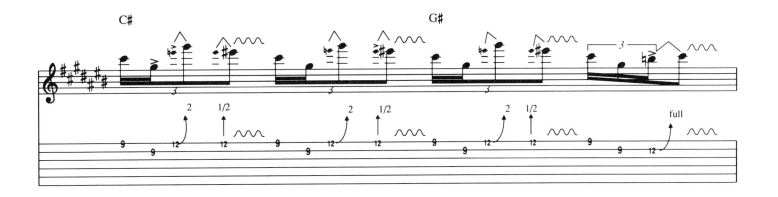

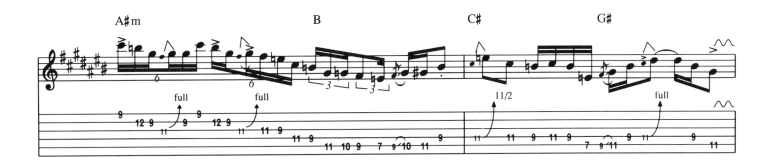

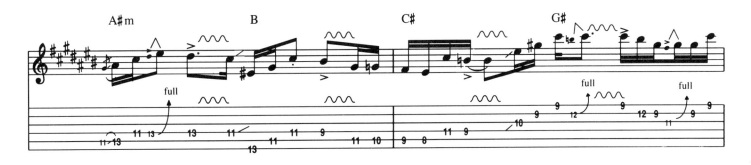

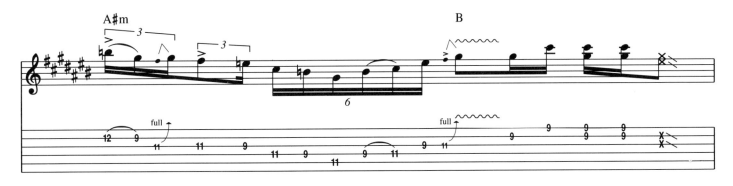

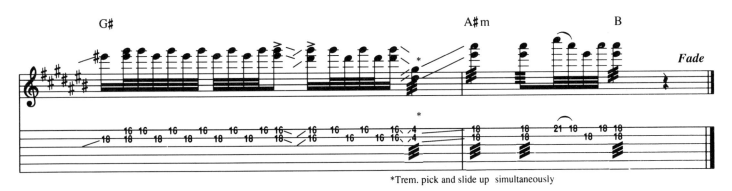

*Trem. pick and slide up simultaneously

UP FROM THE SKIES

Words and Music by JIMI HENDRIX

SPANISH CASTLE MAGIC

Words and Music by JIMI HENDRIX

141

Fade Out

CASTLES MADE OF SAND

Words and Music by JIMI HENDRIX

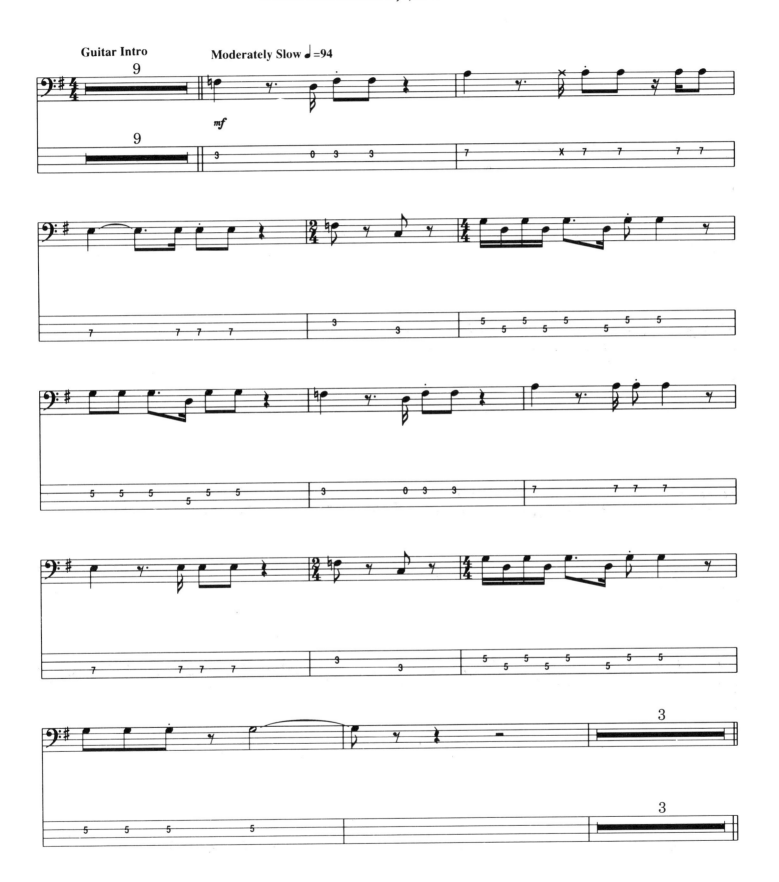

2nd Verse

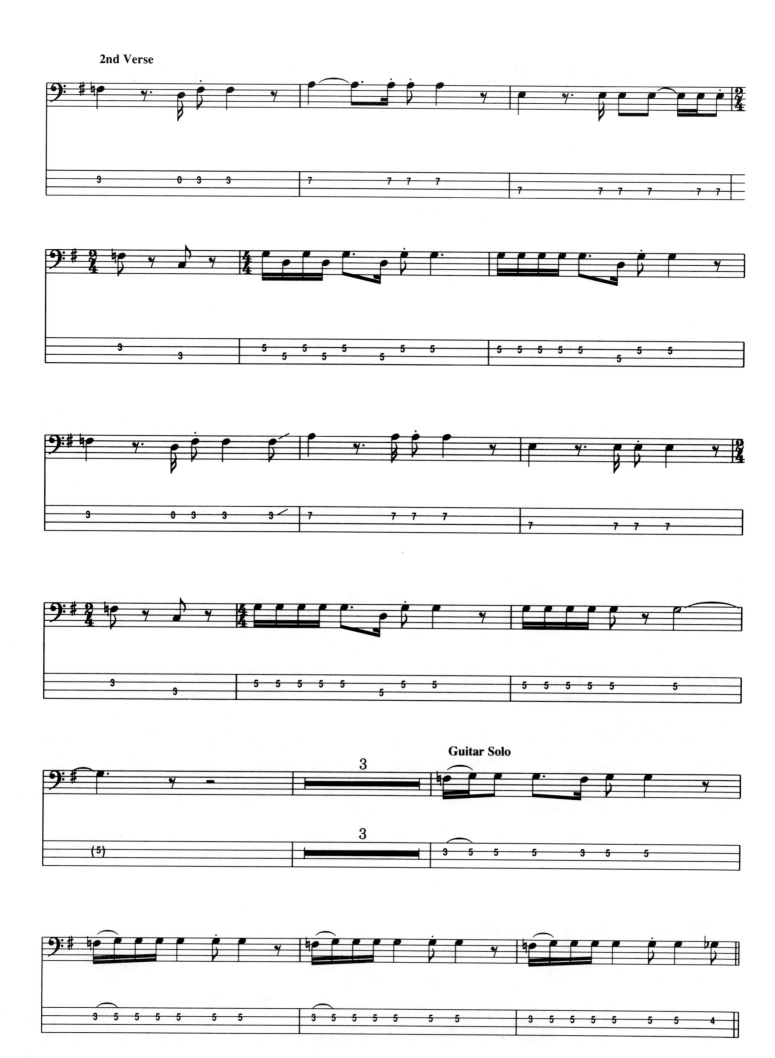

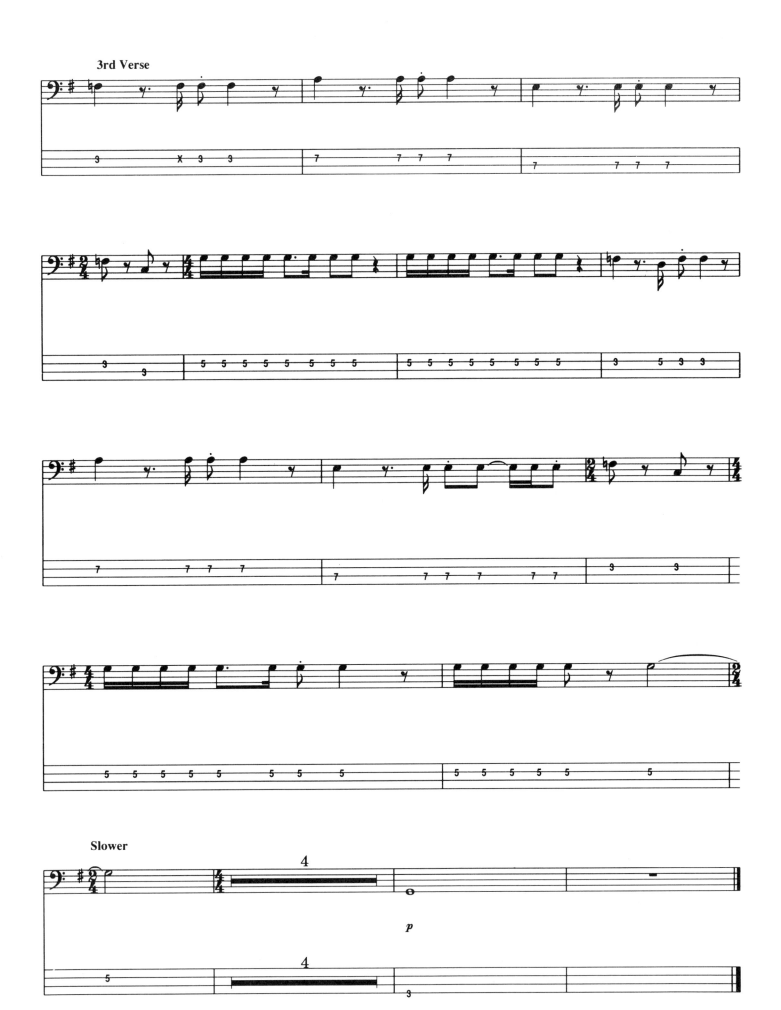

3rd Verse

Slower

WAIT UNTIL TOMORROW

Words and Music by JIMI HENDRIX

2nd Verse

Chorus

148

AIN'T NO TELLING

Words and Music by JIMI HENDRIX

Tune Down 1/2 step

Intro

Moderately

2nd Verse

LITTLE WING

Words and Music by JIMI HENDRIX

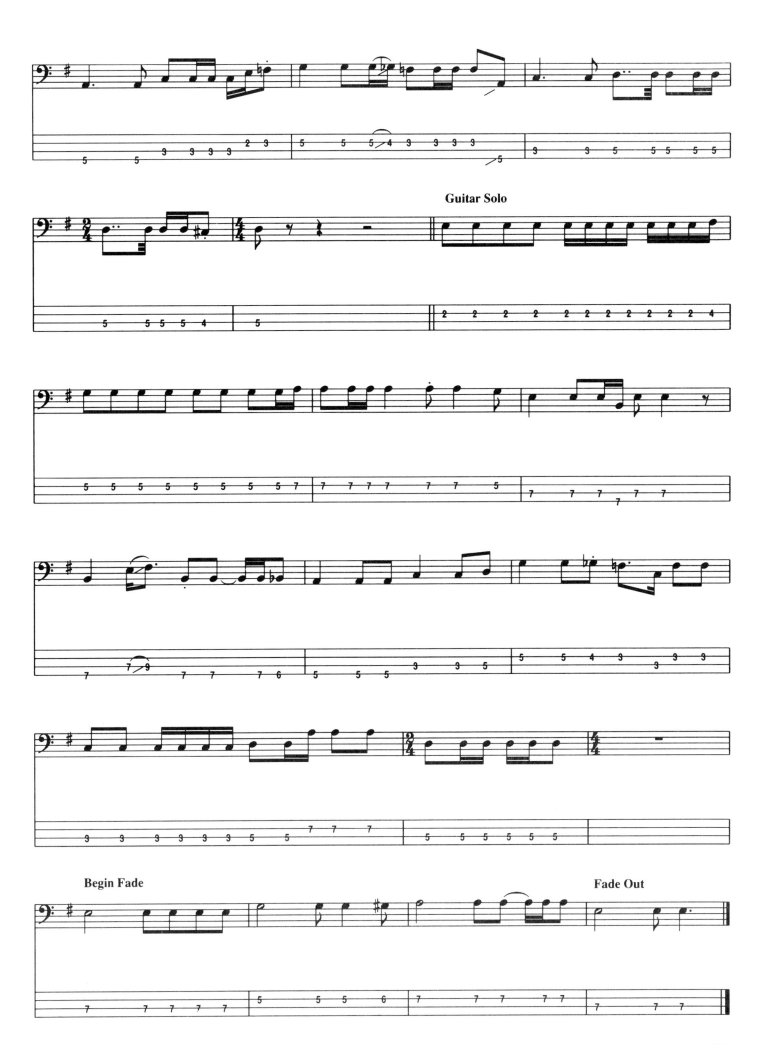

Guitar Solo

Begin Fade

Fade Out

IF 6 WAS 9

Words and Music by JIMI HENDRIX

Bass Tune Down 1/2 step
Introduction

Slow Rock ♩=72

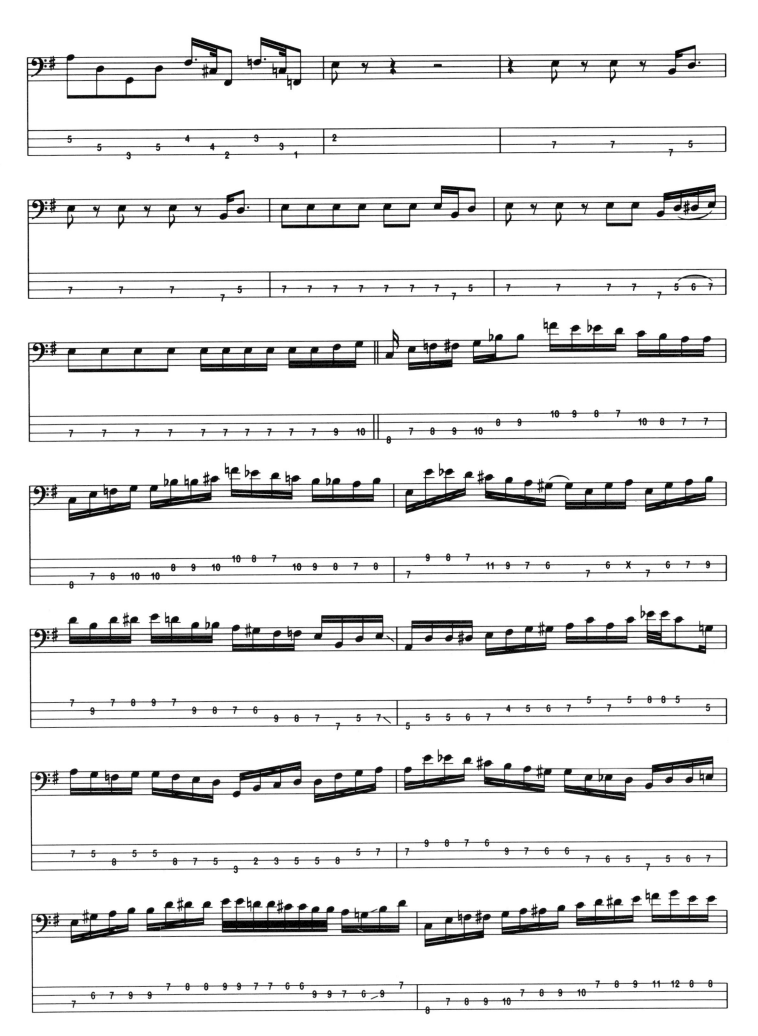

YOU GOT ME FLOATIN'

Words and Music by JIMI HENDRIX

Bass Tune Down 1/2 step
Introduction

Moderate Rock ♩=120

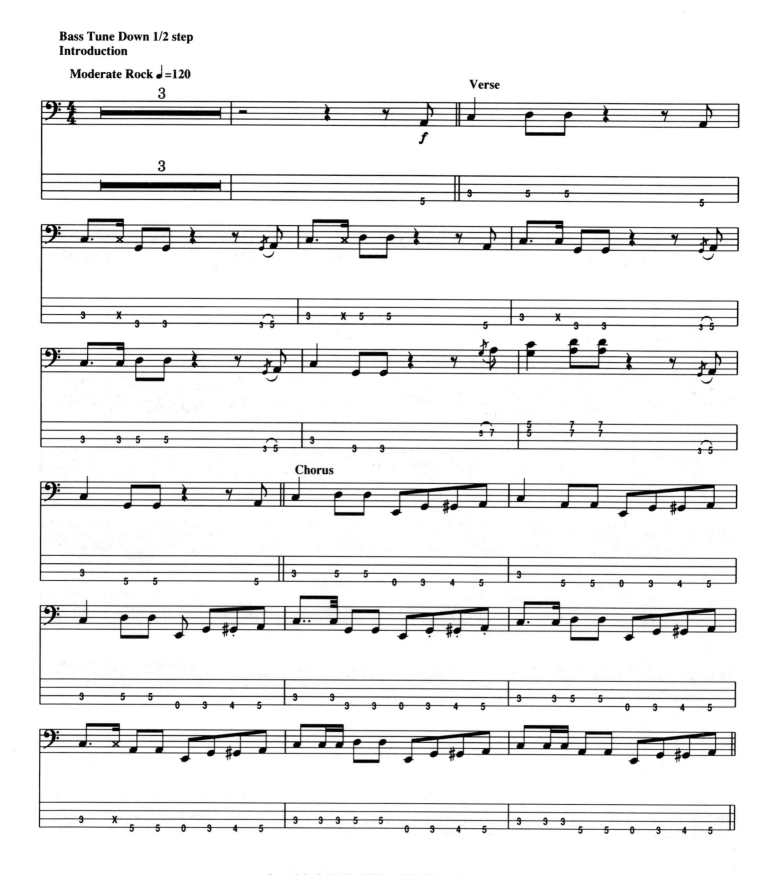

Chorus

Verse

SHE'S SO FINE

Words and Music by NOEL REDDING

Bass Tune Down 1/2 step
Introduction

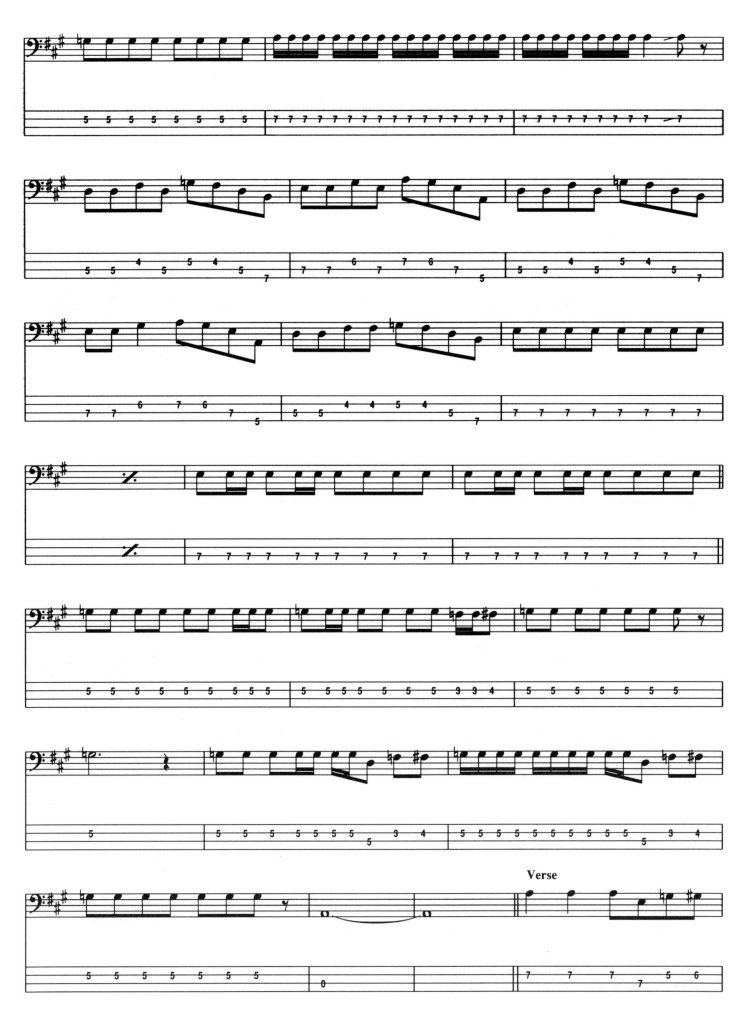

Verse

165

ONE RAINY WISH

Words and Music by JIMI HENDRIX

2nd Verse

Repeat & Fade

LITTLE MISS LOVER

Words and Music by JIMI HENDRIX

BOLD AS LOVE

Words and Music by JIMI HENDRIX

Drum Fill

174

Begin Fade

fade out

UP FROM THE SKIES

Words and Music by JIMI HENDRIX

Begin slow fade

YOU GOT ME FLOATIN'

Words and Music by JIMI HENDRIX

(bass out)

Begin fade

SPANISH CASTLE MAGIC

Words and Music by JIMI HENDRIX

begin fade

WAIT UNTIL TOMORROW

Words and Music by JIMI HENDRIX

187

AIN'T NO TELLING

Words and Music by JIMI HENDRIX

hi-hat

189

LITTLE WING
Words and Music by JIMI HENDRIX

ride cyms

begin fade

SHE'S SO FINE

Words and Music by NOEL REDDING

195

CASTLES MADE OF SAND

Words and Music by JIMI HENDRIX

slower

rit.

ONE RAINY WISH

Words and Music by JIMI HENDRIX

p

mp

(gradually build in volume)

double time feel

200

fade out

LITTLE MISS LOVER

Words and Music by JIMI HENDRIX

BOLD AS LOVE

Words and Music by JIMI HENDRIX

206

IF 6 WAS 9

Words and Music by JIMI HENDRIX

press roll

ride

(leave open)

Hi-hat w/ foot

210

NOTATION LEGEND

Printed and bound in Great Britain by Redwood Books, Trowbridge, Wiltshire

4/96(24059)